Here I am as a baby!

PHOTO HERE

5

FAMILY HISTORY

MY GRANDPARENTS
(YOUR GREAT-GREAT-GRANDPARENTS)

My grandfather's name

My name for him

He was born on

My grandmother's name

My name for her

She was born on

Special things about my grandparents

MY PARENTS (YOUR GREAT-GRANDPARENTS)

My dad's name
....

He was born on
....

An interesting thing about my dad
....

....

....

....

....

My mom's name
....

She was born on
....

An interesting thing about my mom
....

....

....

....

....

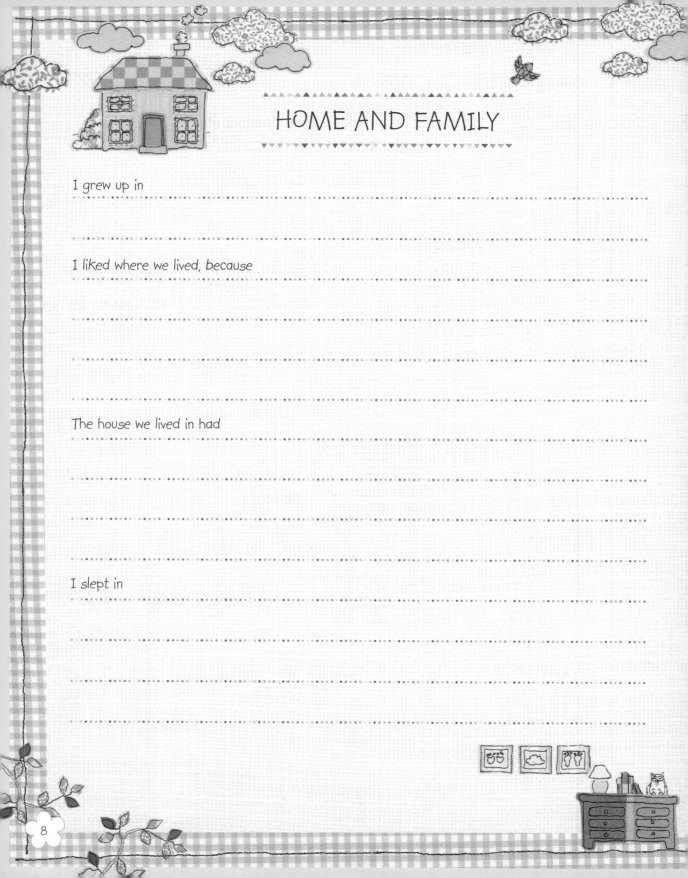

HOME AND FAMILY

I grew up in

....

....

I liked where we lived, because

....

....

....

....

The house we lived in had

....

....

....

....

I slept in

....

....

....

....

The family included (siblings and other relatives)

....
....
....
....

This sums up the kind of family we were

....
....
....
....

My fondest memories of home are

....
....
....
....
....
....

MY CHILDHOOD

BEFORE SCHOOL

I was taken care of mainly by

....

....

....

Sometimes we went to

....

....

....

My favorite food was

....

....

....

A special treat would have been

....

SPECIAL THINGS

My favorite toy was

....

....

....

....

My favorite book was

....

....

....

....

My favorite song was

....

....

....

The first movie I remember watching was

....

....

....

SCHOOL DAYS

The school(s) I went to
....
....
....

We had to wear
....
....

My favorite teacher was
....
....

My favorite subject was
....
....

My least favorite subject was
....
....

The worst thing I ever did at school was
....
....
....
....

Things I am most proud of (grades and achievements)

....

....

....

....

....

I wish I had tried harder in

....

....

....

....

....

If I could go back and do it all again, I would

....

....

....

....

....

CELEBRATIONS

My favorite celebration was

....

....

We celebrated by

....

....

We celebrated birthdays by

....

....

....

A really special occasion in my family was

....

....

....

We celebrated by

....

....

....

It was always a tradition in my family to

....

....

....

VACATIONS

We often spent our vacations
....
....
....
....

This is my favorite memory of a family outing
....
....
....
....

A special trip that I will always remember is
....
....
....
....
....
....

17

CHILDHOOD TREASURES

My most treasured possession was

....

....

I had a collection of

....

....

I saved up to buy

....

....

The best gift I was ever given was

....

....

Some things that I have kept from my childhood

....

....

....

....

....

....

....

CHILDHOOD MEMORIES

My closest friends when I was a child were

....

....

....

....

The worst thing I ever did was

....

....

....

....

The biggest adventure I ever had was

....

....

....

....

Some more special memories of my childhood

....

....

....

....

GROWING UP

FUN

As a teenager, I often went to

....
....

I went with

....
....

My favorite movie was

....
....

My weekends were spent

....
....
....

I got around by

....
....
....

MUSIC

Popular music at the time was

....

....

....

....

The music I liked to listen to was

....

....

....

....

My favorite band/singer was

....

....

....

....

I remember going to see

....

....

....

....

FASHIONS

When I was young, it was fashionable to

....

....

....

....

A style I loved to wear was

....

....

....

....

When I got dressed up, I wore

....

....

....

....

My favorite piece of clothing was

....

....

....

PHOTO HERE

Here I am, looking cool!

My favorite shoes were
....

....

....

My favorite hairstyle was
....

....

....

THE BIG WIDE WORLD

After I finished my education, I

....

....

....

....

....

....

....

I spent my days

....

....

....

....

....

....

....

The things I loved most about growing up were

OUR FAMILY

MEETING YOUR GRANDFATHER

We met at
....

He was   years old
....

I was   years old
....

When I first met him I thought
....

....

On our first date we
....

....

....

26

PHOTO
HERE

One of the first places we visited together was

....

....

Our favorite place to go was

....

....

A special memory of when we got together is

....

....

....

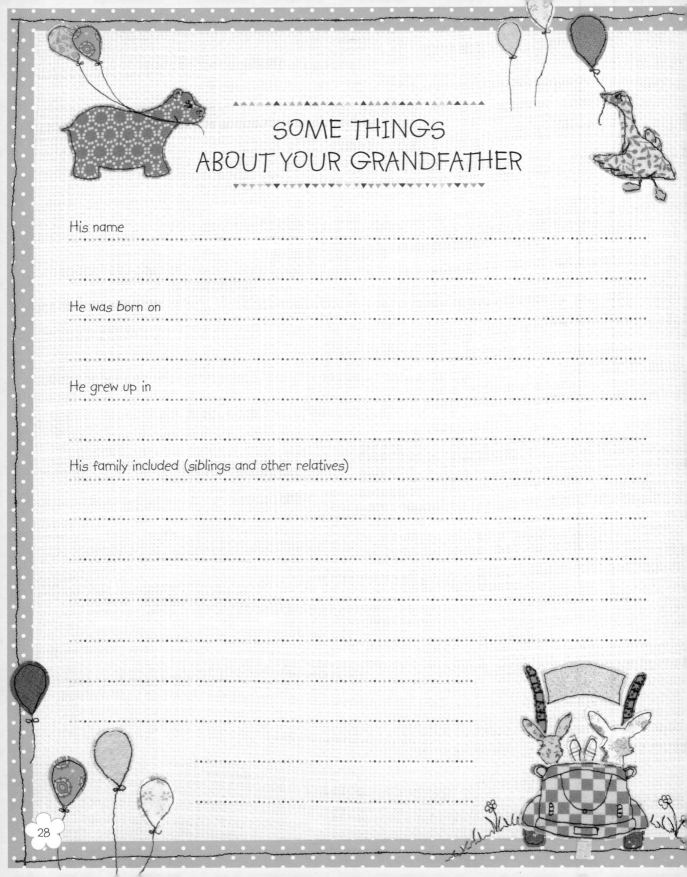

SOME THINGS
ABOUT YOUR GRANDFATHER

His name

....

....

He was born on

....

....

He grew up in

....

....

His family included (siblings and other relatives)

....

....

....

....

....

....

....

PHOTO
HERE

Some things about his family

....

....

....

....

....

....

....

JUST THE TWO OF US

Our first home was

....

....

....

....

I spent my days

....

....

....

He spent his days

....

....

....

In our free time together, we used to enjoy

....

....

....

....

....

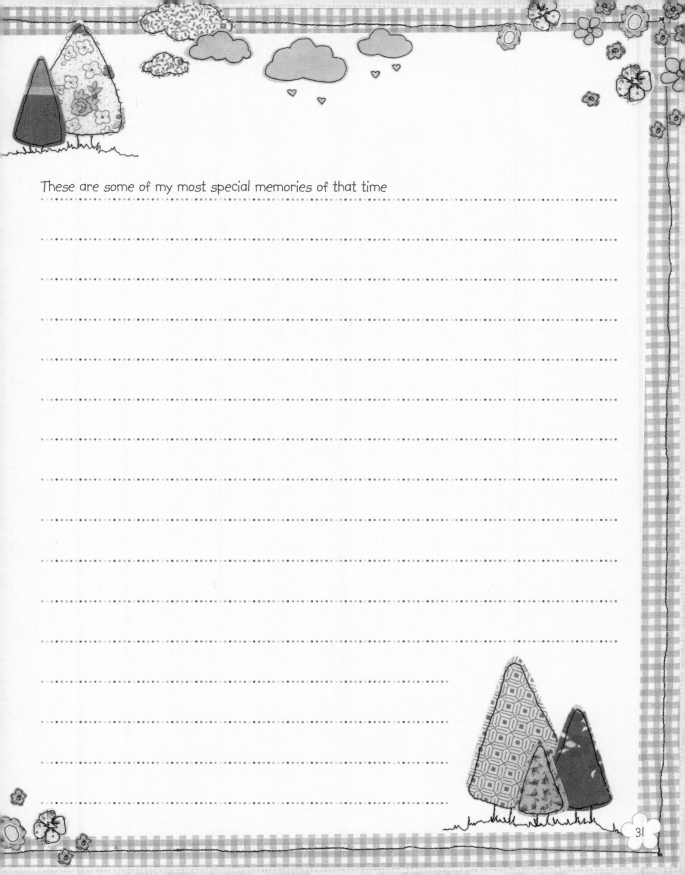

These are some of my most special memories of that time

STARTING A FAMILY

I became pregnant when I was .... years old.

The most wonderful thing about becoming a mom was

PHOTO HERE

33

HOMES

Places and homes we lived in

The place I loved living in the most was

The home I lived in the longest was

FAMILY LIFE

Once I had a family, I spent my days

Some hobbies and pastimes I enjoyed back then

We had fun as a family when we

VACATIONS

We often spent our vacations

....

....

....

We stayed in

....

....

....

The best vacation we had was

....

....

....

A special time that I will always remember is

....

....

....

....

....

....

HAPPY DAYS

These are some of the most wonderful, funny, and memorable moments of family life

BECOMING A GRANDMOTHER

When I became a grandmother I was _____ years old.

The thing I looked forward to the most about being a grandmother was

It feels different from being a mom, because

I first saw you when you were _____ old.

I thought you looked most like

PHOTO HERE

I LOVE

BEING YOUR GRANDMOTHER BECAUSE

THE THINGS YOU HAVE TAUGHT ME

HOW THINGS HAVE CHANGED

Things that are the most different now are

....

....

....

....

....

Things I loved about growing up when I did

....

....

....

....

What I would like most if I were growing up now

....

....

....

....

THINGS I'D LIKE TO SHARE

Always remember that
....

....

Make the most of
....

....

Try to be
....

....

Never forget that
....

....

What matters more than anything is
....

....

A SPECIAL
MESSAGE
FOR YOU

Wonderful times!

Photo
Here

47

This edition published by Parragon Books Ltd in 2015

Parragon Inc.
440 Park Avenue South, 13th Floor
New York, NY 10016
www.parragon.com

Project managed by Annabel King
Production by Fiona Rhys-Griffith
Cover and internal illustrations by Annabelle Ozanne
Written by Cath Ard
Cover design by Karli Skelton
Internal design by Emily Lewis

CUTE AS A BUTTON is a trademark of
Parragon Books Ltd and is a registered UK trademark.

ISBN: 978-1-4723-7652-7

Printed in China